HIV-AIDS STIGMA

What the Church needs to know

A portion of the proceeds of
this book will be donated to:
Friends of Canon Gideon Foundation in Kampala, Uganda

Revd. Michael Angley Ogwuche

**Foreword by
Canon Gideon Byamugisha**

British Library Cataloguing in Publication Data.
A catalogue record for this book is available from the British Library

ISBN 978 0 86071 695 2

A Commissioned Publication of

MOORLEYS
Print & Publishing
tel: 0115 932 0643 web: www.moorleys.co.uk

Dedication

To
Nancy Áanya Ofikwu
…and Others

Acknowledgements

I deeply appreciate Canon Gideon Byamugisha for his immense contributions, the Revd. C. Paschal Eze, (USA), for his insight, the Revd. Daniel Kodjo French of the Methodist Church, Wigan for his pastoral advice; Dr. Geoffrey Carr (PhD), for his confidence in me *(though he is deceased, his works live on),* and Bishop Dennis Tanner, Scotland, for all his encouragements.

I am thankful to the Institute of Counselling in Glasgow for all their support for this project. Allison Cooper (Registrar of Cliff College) and Moorleys Print & Publishing (Derbyshire, England).

I heartily thank my dear wife Christiana, for her enduring love, support and encouragement in all I have ever desired to be.

Most of all, I appreciate the teaching of Jesus Christ who taught us not only to love ourselves but to love others as well.

HIV-AIDS:
What the Church needs to know

Contents

Foreword

Good News Delayed Is Good News Denied

The good news of improved scientific knowledge and techniques, and more expertise in the area of HIV and AIDS prevention that has accumulated over the last 30 years of confronting and engaging the epidemic is tempered with the reality that this good news has not been translated into reduced infections, transmissions and deaths amongst key affected populations, age groups and families in the most at-risk and most affected communities and regions of the world. This includes most of Africa, parts of Asia and Eastern Europe, Latin America and the Caribbean as well as the educationally underserved, socially marginalised and economically deprived demographics of Europe and North America.

In countries and communities where state, interstate and non-state partnerships have worked to reduce the **S**tigma, **S**hame, **D**enial, **D**iscrimination, **I**naction and 'Mis-action' (**SSDDIM**) related to HIV; and to multiply the **s**afe behaviours and practices, **a**ccess to treatment and good nutrition; **v**oluntary, routine and stigma-sensitive counselling and **e**mpowerment of those individuals, families and communities at risk (**SAVE**), progress to successfully reverse the HIV epidemic and eliminate new infections is on track. In others, where the theology, pastoral practice, legislation and policy environments work to increase SSDDIM and reduce SAVE, efforts to match on-the-ground programs with scientific gains in HIV and AIDS prevention among the key populations negatively affected by such theologies, practices, legislation and environments are painfully slow. As a result, we still see a situation where, even with the knowledge and science required to prevent sexual and non-sexual HIV transmission is well established, depressing news of continuing HIV infections, transmissions, illnesses and preventable deaths continue to fill our TV screens, newspapers and the 'new HIV incidence' surveillance briefs received by policy makers.

This is why this book is both important and timely: to serve the theological, pastoral and prophetic voice and public health imperative to reduce and defeat HIV- and AIDS-related stigma that sustains and fuels socio-cultural, religious, economic and legislative barriers to reaching zero new HIV infections, zero discrimination and zero AIDS-related deaths, faster, smarter and more effectively.

In many communities and countries, the HIV- and AIDS-related stigma only serves to worsen the epidemic by undermining HIV testing, disclosure of an HIV-positive status and, therefore, timely access to prevention and treatment services. The stigma causes faith communities to ignore, disparage and discriminate against those who need care and attention most. The stigma causes a false sense of security among young people, couples and parents in the general population who incorrectly believe they are not at risk when, in reality, they are living, growing up, marrying and producing children in risky environments with high HIV incidence and prevalence. Only a faith-led, faith-inspired, faith-based and theologically informed campaign to reduce the stigma can effectively and quickly accelerate HIV and AIDS prevention for safer and healthier living among God's people.

Religious Law, Public Legislation and Stigma
Rather than assisting in the achievement of the goals set by local, national and international communities in slowing the spread of HIV, many of the current legal and regulatory terrains in popular theology (on which most constitutional laws, interventions and community practices in at-risk countries and communities are hinged) are actually working actively to undermine HIV prevention and treatment among the most vulnerable and most affected age groups, families and communities.[1]

As a result, specialist scientists, public health practitioners, religious leaders and community members are often working in theological, legal and policy environments that are structured to hinder good public health interventions, stigmatising and marginalising the same people whom the good health programs seek to support; thereby preventing safer, healthier, more peaceful, more prosperous and more spiritually satisfying living.

I am very optimistic that this book will help us as faith communities, religious leaders, congregations and theological training institutions to generate enough moral responsibility, pastoral duty, theological justification and prophetic voice imperative to not only advocate and disseminate accurate knowledge and science about the HIV epidemic, but also to do more and do better against HIV-related stigma, shame, denial, discrimination, inaction and 'mis-action'.

---

[1] Aziza Ahmed (United States), Assistant Professor of Law, Northeastern University School of Law, address to the 7th International AIDS Society Conference on HIV Pathogenesis, Treatment & Prevention 29–30th June, 2013, Kuala Lumpar.

I hope and pray that this book evokes among us greater theological responsibility for creating, supporting and sustaining a legal and policy landscape that:

a) does not discriminate against, stigmatise or marginalise the very at-risk families, communities and population groups who need more of our support, accompaniment and care than our blame and ridicule

b) effectively tackles social determinants of risk, vulnerability and ill-health, while modelling and advocating structural interventions that are key to turning the tide of HIV in Africa, Asia, Latin America, the Caribbean and parts of Europe and North America.

"May the God of peace, who through the blood of the eternal covenant brought back from the dead our Lord Jesus, that great Shepherd of the sheep, equip you with everything good you need for doing His will effectively, and may He work in us what is pleasing to Him, through Jesus Christ, to whom be glory forever and ever. *Amen*". (Hebrews 13:20–21)

Rev Canon Dr Gideon B Byamugisha
Kampala, Uganda

Prologue

While studying at Cliff College, England, in 2001 I came across a piece of information about the XIV International AIDS conference organised by the International Aids Society, one of the world's biggest organisers of HIV and AIDS conferences. I applied to serve as a volunteer and was accepted and travelled out to Barcelona. This conference changed my life forever.

During the conference, some Christian participants, including myself, decided to meet at a Cathedral in the city to discuss how the Church can engage in the fight against HIV and AIDS in a more meaningful way and from a Christian perspective. Here I met Canon Gideon Byamugisha, the first African Clergyman to publicly declare his HIV-positive status.

As I shook hands with the Canon during the introduction, I couldn't help wondering why a member of the clergy would be HIV-positive in the first place and was afraid of becoming infected by his touch. I was completely ignorant, like thousands of Christians and Christian leaders across the board, and did not know at that time that you cannot become infected by a touch or a hug. I was also ignorant of the fact that we are all at risk simply because we are humans. Little did I know that I was directly and mentally stigmatising the Clergyman and I was unaware of this stigmatisation until someone educated me. I believe this is the case with many Christians and Church leaders today.

From that moment onwards, I resolved not to stigmatise anyone again and I firmly resolved to join the fight against HIV and AIDS stigma within the Church and the larger community. I have, since then, continued to give presentations on the subject around the world and Canon Gideon Byamugisha and I are now both comrades-in-arms in the war against the HIV and AIDS pandemic.

Revd. Michael Angley Ogwuche
Glasgow, Scotland

CHAPTER 1
The HIV and AIDS Invasion

There are various theories surrounding the origin of the HIV virus. However, the common and generally accepted theory is that it may have originated from a species of chimpanzee commonly found in the West/Central African region.

The HIV virus could have been transferred to humans from the chimpanzees and monkeys kept around many households for food or even as pets. When attempting to capture these animals, it is not unusual for blood exchange to occur between the hunter and the hunted.

The Sub-Saharan African region is notorious for its 'bush meat' markets where meat products from such animals as chimpanzees and monkeys are easily obtained. This may also contribute greatly to the transfusion of blood from animals to humans, more so because of the lack of proper methods of slaughtering and processing.

Although the earliest documentary evidence of HIV dates back to the latter part of the 1950s, it was not until 1981 that the New York Times reported an outbreak of a rare form of cancer among homosexuals in New York and California. At that early stage of discovery, it was generally referred to as 'gay cancer' but was subsequently identified as Kaposi's sarcoma and then as HIV-AIDS and has remained one of the greatest health challenges of our time.

CHAPTER 2
Understanding HIV and AIDS

It is crucial in the fight against the disease that people in our various churches clearly understand what HIV-AIDS is all about; only a clear understanding will help to reduce the stigma and further spread of the pandemic. Distinguishing between HIV and AIDS can be difficult for most people; they are not the same thing. The differences will be explained as we progress in this book.

It is possible for a person to have the Human Immunodeficiency Virus (HIV) for many years and still appear healthy, which explains why the virus can easily be passed to another person unknowingly. That is why it is important to take personal responsibility by knowing your status and protecting yourself against possible infection by the virus.

HIV is the virus that causes AIDS and it can survive and replicate itself in the human body. This extremely dangerous virus mainly attacks cells in the immune system, thus preventing people from naturally fighting off various diseases. When this happens, they quite often become ill but it is still possible not to result in AIDS, especially if well managed with appropriate medication. The only way to find out if a person has HIV is to undergo a simple test where a health professional takes a small sample of your blood and sends it to a specialist laboratory for testing. HIV testing is confidential, meaning that the health professional will usually not tell anyone about the test without your consent. In most countries, the test is free.

A person should consider having an HIV test if they have had unprotected sex, shared drug injecting equipment, been exposed to HIV during a medical procedure or think there is a possibility of having been exposed to HIV in some other way.

Although many people are very uneasy about taking an HIV test just in case the result is positive, knowing one's HIV status has some benefits. One such benefit is early treatment. If a person knows they are infected with HIV, they can seek medical help before the symptoms appear. They can also help to prevent the spread of the virus by taking necessary precautions. Testing early will put their mind at rest. Conversely, a late diagnosis may result in less effective treatment. It's extremely important to remember that if a person tests negative, they should do all in their power to stay safe – and encourage others in that regard.

Contrary to popular belief, a positive HIV result is not a death sentence. Professional care and support are usually available and, although there is still no cure for HIV, treatments can keep the virus under control and the immune system healthy. People on appropriate HIV treatment can still live a healthy, active life. Though there may be some side effects, antiretroviral drugs are known to have greatly improved the health of those living with the virus, delaying or even preventing the progress of HIV, and providing those with AIDS the opportunity for recovery. As a result, their average life expectancy has greatly improved.

Yet, these drugs are unaffordable to many who need them in a number of countries. The fact that antiretroviral therapies are very expensive – from Sub-Saharan Africa to Latin America – should be of great concern to the global Christian community. One of the constructive steps churches could take is to lend their voices to the ongoing campaign to enable people, especially in developing countries, to gain much-needed access to these drugs. Doing so will help to save and sustain precious lives.

CHAPTER 3
Can a Person of Faith Fall Ill?

To Christians faith in God is very important but many also like to think that because they believe in God they cannot fall ill and, if they do, they should and must be healed. That is not the case. There is much evidence in the Bible and in our community of faith today of physicians and others falling ill.

In the book of Matthew, we are told the mother-in-law of the foremost Apostle of Jesus Christ, Peter, experienced sickness and was healed by Jesus Christ. 'When Jesus arrived at Peter's house, Peter's mother-in-law was sick in bed with a high fever' (Matthew 8:14; New Living Translation, 2007).

Also, we find Jesus making reference to human suffering, including sickness: 'Then they too will answer, "Lord, when did we see you hungry or thirsty or a stranger, or naked or sick or in prison, and did not give you whatever you needed?"' (Matthew 25:44). Some Christians believe seeking medical help demonstrates a lack of faith in God and that to do so may prevent God from healing the individual. The human body, as we know, experiences wear and tear, more so if it is not properly taken care of. For example, it is possible to get very sick as a result of malnutrition or overeating. I personally know a very committed Christian who became ill with cancer and later died even after incessant supplication on his behalf to God. Did that demonstrate a lack of faith in God?

I don't think so. That God permitted the sickness should also not be construed as God's punishment but rather a demonstration of God's grace to bear. The Apostle Paul pointed this out in his letter to the Corinthians: 'But he said to me, "My grace is sufficient for you, for my power is made perfect in weakness." Therefore I will boast all the more gladly about my weaknesses, so that Christ's power may rest on me. That is why, for Christ's sake, I delight in weaknesses, in insults, in hardships, in persecutions, in difficulties. For when I am weak, then I am strong' (2 Corinthians 12:9–10).

Suppose you are involved in a car crash, do you expect to be rushed to the Accident and Emergency Ward of a nearby hospital or to writhe in pain and die in the mangled car? In my early days of ministry, a very close minister friend of mine rushed his sick child to the hospital for treatment but felt he had to lie to his Church about it. Do I believe in the miracle of healing? My answer is 'yes'.

Do I believe it is wrong to seek a qualified medical doctor's help when someone is sick? My answer is 'no'.

It is, therefore, not the case that God cannot perform miracles of healing but it is the case that we should not always expect God to act according to our own dictates. God has given these medical doctors great knowledge and skill to assist us when we need them.

In the Bible, there are scriptures that make references to physicians. Perhaps one of the most popular ones is found in Paul's letter to the Colossians: 'Our dear friend Luke, the doctor, and Demas send greetings' (Colossians 4:14). It is important for Christians to know that even when we have to visit a doctor, our ultimate faith should be in God, not the doctor. As a doctor may say to a patient 'I'm sorry, I cannot heal you, but I can only treat you.' In other words, only God can heal but the doctor helps you to better understand the nature of the sickness and offers you valuable advice and support on controlling and managing it.

However, there are also wonderful verses to refer to when talking about medical treatment from a biblical perspective such as: Luke 10:34, James 5:14, Isaiah 1:6, Jeremiah 8:22 and Ezekiel 47:12, amongst others.

So, can a person of faith fall ill? The answer is absolutely YES. Should a person of faith trust God for healing? The answer is absolutely YES. And should a person of faith go to doctor? The answer is also absolutely YES. There is nothing wrong with seeking help from the doctors and, of course, trusting God to grant such doctors the knowledge and wisdom they need to treat you well.

CHAPTER 4
Why are HIV and AIDS Viewed Differently?

Why are HIV and AIDS viewed differently from all other classifications of illness? HIV and AIDS are misconstrued because of the association with supposed promiscuity. Many people, especially Christians, view HIV and AIDS as a disease designed for those who have low morals but they often ignore the basic fact that HIV is not only transmitted through sexual intercourse, though that is the major route the virus takes into the human body.

There are several other ways the virus can be contracted/transmitted:
- through contact with blood or sexual fluid of an infected person
- unprotected vaginal and anal sex with an infected person
- oral sex (said to present low risk unless there is contact with the sexual fluids of the infected person with a sore or cut in the mouth)
- sharing syringes without sterilisation (it is always advisable not to share a needle, syringe or any sharp object capable of piercing the body)
- blood transfusion (since many countries now take the issue of blood screening very seriously, the risk of transmission from blood is minimal)
- mother to child (the virus can be passed from a mother to a child in the womb, during childbirth or through breast feeding)
- tattooing and body piercing when instruments are not properly sterilised
- sharing razor blades if unsterilised.

It behoves individuals to take absolute care when dealing with blood.

Religious rituals
I was once asked by a Church leader if HIV can spread through religious rites like immersion baptism and Holy Communion. My answer was and still remains 'no'. Sharing a pool of water or communion cup is safe. So, a minister need not be afraid, just as recipients who are HIV positive and those who are not, should not be ashamed or afraid to participate in these rituals. The virus cannot jump out of the body of the carrier without a cut or body fluid.

Simply put, no minister of the gospel should allow ignorance of HIV and AIDS to make him/her appear fidgety when administering water baptism or Holy Communion as it could make someone who is HIV-positive feel stigmatised.

CHAPTER 5
HIV and AIDS: A Christian Response

There is no Bible verse that directly addresses HIV and AIDS. Wondering why? The answer is simple: Diseases like HIV and AIDS were not in existence at that time.

However, Jesus Christ did touch the afflicted of His day. Similarly, He is calling His Church today to reach out with compassion to those devastated by HIV-AIDS and suffering in our Churches and communities. If Christ truly lives in us, we should also be full of compassion for those suffering. We can touch, pray and comfort them. We can and should be there for them without being judgmental.

Jesus was full of compassion

Would Jesus act differently if He were here bodily? Again, the answer will be 'no'. Jesus was always full of compassion for people everywhere He went; Jesus had pity for the suffering and was ever ready with a very strong desire to help. 'Now a leper came to him and fell to his knees, asking for help. "If you are willing, you can make me clean," he said. Moved with compassion, Jesus stretched out his hand and touched him, saying, "I am willing. Be clean!" The leprosy left him at once, and he was clean' (Mark 1:40–42, New English Translation). According to the UNAIDS World AIDS Day Report 2012, AIDS is still a leading cause of death in the world today. About 34 million people are estimated to be living with HIV-AIDS worldwide. The trouble is that most of them do not know they are infected and may be spreading the virus to others.

Sadly too, despite the devastating impact of this pandemic, many surprisingly know little about HIV-AIDS and its transmission. Few in the Church have developed a thoughtful, biblical response to those ravaged by this disease, and many in the Church are not bothered as they feel it is 'their disease, not ours'. Much of the Church's fear about HIV-AIDS emanates from a lack of basic understanding of how the disease is transmitted.

Some church people view HIV-AIDS as a disease for homosexuals. They incorrectly believe that HIV-AIDS is punishment from God. That is not the case as HIV-AIDS may or may not be the consequence of sin. The disease has no respect for age, sexual behaviour or social boundaries. We are all at risk because we are all humans. That's why it is very unfair to treat people living with HIV-AIDS differently.

This section is the main thrust of the publication since we are dealing with how the Church can respond to the whole issue of stigma surrounding HIV and AIDS. Stigma is simply any mark, scar, stain or moral blemish. Theology in relative terms is an attempt to understand God through study.

The word theology basically refers to the systematic and <u>rational</u> study of concepts of <u>God</u> and the nature of religious truths. But since it can be used as exegesis of thoughts regarding the Church, I chose to employ it to suit my purpose here, hence the phraseology STIGMATISATION THEOLOGY. In the early days of the discovery of the ravaging effects of HIV and AIDS, a good number of Christians and Christian leaders worldwide propagated stigmatisation theology stating that HIV-AIDS was a punishment from God.

Gillian Paterson, a renowned HIV-AIDS activist, in one of her presentations asserts that "A further challenge comes from the Church's traditional teachings on ethical matters. Jesus was extremely wary of religion that is defined by moral codes and rules. Christ's free gift to our world is grace, and the unconditional love of God. And yet, many churches have greeted the issue of HIV and AIDS with thundering moral denunciations and by victimising and excluding those who are known to be living with HIV and their families.

You have sinned, say their leaders; you deserve to die. When the Church takes this view, it is indeed more part of the problem than part of the solution. In effect it is saying, go away, you who labour and are heavy-laden. There is no rest for you here". Sometimes one wonders what the Church of Christ did with the unmerited favour of God which persuaded Jesus to die in our place in the first instance. The Church preaches grace, yet some churches have no grace when it comes to giving grace. The Bible clearly states: 'For God so loved the world that He gave his one and only Son, that whoever believes in Him shall not perish but have eternal life' (John 3:16).

Christians are called to exercise this same grace that informed the response of Jesus when confronted about the greatest commandment. He replied: 'Love the Lord your God with all your heart and with all your soul and with all your mind. This is the first and greatest commandment. And the second is like it: Love your neighbour as yourself. All the Law and the Prophets hang on these two commandments' (Matthew 22:39-40).

Thus, if Christians truly love the Lord with all their heart, soul and mind, they will also love themselves deeply, and if they so love themselves, they will deeply love all those who are victims of conditions such as HIV and AIDS, realising that anybody could have been a victim.

The true test of Christianity is how we respond to the needs of others around us – from oppression, poverty and hunger, to HIV and AIDS. As a Church, we have no theological or moral right whatsoever to stigmatise anyone because of their physical condition.

After all, everything that is corruptible will be transformed as God's word declares: 'For the perishable must clothe itself with the imperishable, and the mortal with immortality' (1 Corinthians 15:53). The Bible again says: 'Whatever you did for one of the least of these brothers of mine, you did for me' (Matthew 25:38–40). As a Church, the way and manner we treat the fight against this pandemic is crucial to the success we can achieve as 'salt of the earth' and 'light of the world' (Matthew 5:13–14).

XIV International AIDS Conference Barcelona, Spain 2002

HIV&AIDS Presentation at Heifer Int. HQ,
Arkansas USA 2008

XVIII International AIDS Conference Vienna, Austria 2010

Councillor Flannigan joined
Revd. Michael Angley Ogwuche to mark World Aids Day 2010

Glasgow Afro-Caribbean Community Conversation on HIV/AIDS

XVIII International AIDS Conference, Vienna

The Author, Canon Byamugisha and Christy
Faith and Health Conference, Glasgow

Jubilee Social Centre's HIV/AIDS Reframed DVD

Rev. Ben, The Author, Christy and Canon Byamugisha
Faith and Health Conference, Glasgow

CHAPTER 6
Stigmatisation Theology

Positive attitude towards HIV-positive people

According to Canon Gideon Byamugisha, 'With HIV/AIDS, it is not the condition itself that hurts most (because many other diseases and conditions lead to serious suffering and death), but the stigma and the possibility of rejection and discrimination, misunderstanding and loss of trust that HIV-positive people have to deal with'.

People living with HIV are particularly vulnerable to discrimination, as HIV remains a highly stigmatised condition. At least one in three people diagnosed with HIV has experienced HIV-related discrimination at some time.

The question then is: how can the Church help to reduce stigma and discrimination among its rank and file? This can be done by educating Church people and their leaders (priests, ministers, pastors, etc.) about the rights of people living with HIV and by preaching and teaching young and adult members to bring about a change in attitude.

The 2003 World Church Report states, 'Within Churches, HIV and AIDS need to be talked about honestly and openly by all members of the Church. Church leaders must include HIV and AIDS in their theology in a way that will increase people's awareness and decrease stigma and discrimination against those affected by HIV-AIDS and enable people to give care and comfort to those affected'.

HIV-AIDS stigma and discrimination are a global problem that the Church needs to challenge, being an agent of change. Stigma manifests itself differently in our communities, religious bodies and among individuals. Stigma and discrimination are commonly directed towards those involved in activities considered as antisocial, such as drug addiction, prostitution, etc.

The effect of stigma is devastating as it makes it more difficult for people trying to come to terms with their condition and their ability to manage their disease on a personal level. It also greatly hinders attempts to fight the rapid spread of AIDS as individuals become reluctant to seek help.

Ban Ki Moon, UN Secretary-General, says: 'Stigma remains the single most important barrier to public action. It is a main reason why too many people are afraid to see a doctor to determine whether they have the disease, or to seek treatment if so.

'It helps make AIDS the silent killer, because people fear the social disgrace of speaking about it, or taking easily-available precautions. Stigma is a chief reason why the AIDS epidemic continues to devastate societies around the world.'

Dissecting the stigma

AIDS-related stigma has a strong bearing on individual and collective ability to fight the pandemic, hence it has the potential for stopping the progress of efforts already made towards controlling and possibly eradicating the disease. Informed research shows that stigma and discrimination are the major reasons people are reluctant to be tested, to disclose their HIV status or to take medications. Unwillingness to take an HIV test means that people who otherwise should have received help don't get help, or are diagnosed late when the virus has taken full residence in their body, thereby making treatment less effective and causing an early death that could have been prevented.

There are several types of stigma and discrimination facing people living with HIV and AIDS in our society. However, they can be divided into three groups for the purpose of this book.

1. *Self-stigma*

This entails believing, assimilating and internalising negative attitudes, reactions and actions from others. As a result, the individual fails to appreciate themselves and incessantly blames themselves for what has happened, which may lead to an endless circle of depression. Fear of negative community reaction can greatly hinder personal efforts to seek help early by solidifying the wall of silence and shame surrounding the disease.

2. *Stigma by association*

In many cases, other members of the (nuclear and extended) family of an infected individual are also affected by stigma. People callously judge the entire family, blaming them for what has happened to their relative. This type of stigmatisation happens just because they are associated with a person infected by HIV and AIDS. It is important therefore that the Church clearly understands that it may or may not be the fault of the individual or the family and is prepared to help the infected person and those affected to overcome the hurtful stigma.

3. *Societal Stigma*

People sometimes wrongly or inaccurately blame others for their conditions and misfortunes.

Other consequences of HIV and AIDS stigma and discrimination include depression and feelings of isolation, rejection, condemnation, being forgotten and useless. In some cases, people with HIV-AIDS are kicked out of their family, work, rented accommodation and membership organisation by fellow Christians. A number of them are also known to have dropped out of school or jobs, owing to the deluge of insults, teasing and ridicule they were subjected to. Others have unfortunately resorted to alcoholism, drug abuse and suicide.

Again, society and the media tend to frequently emphasise that only promiscuous people contract AIDS and should, therefore, be blamed for their misfortune. However, HIV does not require a person to be sexually promiscuous in order to infect them. Judging someone's sexual behaviour because they are HIV positive is of great consequence and it is always important for the Church or members of the community to be aware, as stated earlier in this book, HIV can also be passed on by other means and not only through sexual contact with an infected person. For instance, it can be transmitted by sharing needles, from mother to baby, by receiving infected blood products, etc.

CHAPTER 7
Why the Church must take Action

One study presented at the International AIDS Society AIDS conference in Mexico by Terry-Ann Smith-Frith, a procurement officer with the Jamaica Ministry of Health's HIV and AIDS Prevention and Control Project, said that next to public health workers, religious leaders are the most discriminatory against infected individuals.

Terry-Ann Smith-Frith noted that infected people were not allowed to take communion in some churches where one cup was used for all members of the congregation.

They were also advised against marriage and, in some instances, not baptised in the church pool. 'One young lady had to go to the river to get baptised, as the pastor would not baptise her in the church pool with others.' She also observed that the situation is made worse as some infected Christians are shunned when they seek pastoral counselling.

'They are suddenly told they can no longer sing in the choir and that they must now sit in the back of the church.'

These alleged violations by Church leaders are appalling and may have resulted from the die-hard belief that the disease is a lifestyle problem and so the infected person is to be blamed. The real question begging to be answered is: how do we reconcile the attitude of some Church people with biblical examples of Jesus' compassionate lifestyle?

We believe the Church, as a faith-based institution, has the potential to reach people on a massive scale and the ability to influence positive behaviour in society.

It is, therefore, an important arena in the fight against further spread of the pandemic, especially the stigmatisation of those affected within our community. We cannot afford to underestimate the power of the Church as an agent of change.

In a statement the former Archbishop of Canterbury said, 'This pandemic has reached alarming proportions, affecting and infecting many who have not the knowledge or the personal autonomy to avoid transmission.' In order to win this fight against HIV and AIDS, Church leaders must continue to explore appropriate ways to incorporate AIDS education in their teaching, with the aim of reducing the stigma and discrimination associated with the disease. If Church leaders take the issues of HIV and AIDS as seriously as they take their numerical growth, it will go a long way in slowing the progress of AIDS, especially in reducing stigma and discrimination.

A February 2007 report by the World Health Organisation (WHO) at the National Cathedral in Washington DC states that faith-based organisations (FBO) 'play much a greater role in HIV and AIDS care and treatment in sub-Saharan Africa than previously recognised'. The report concludes that 'greater coordination and better communication are urgently needed between organisations of different faiths and the private and public health sectors'. In recognition of the potential of the Church, church leaders must endeavour to unleash energy within and apply it to the fight in a way that has never before been seen.

However, this cannot happen unless the Church recognises that something has to be done.

Church leaders should be willing to take a leading role in reducing the stigma and subsequently ending the progress of HIV and AIDS by actively supporting prevention, treatment and care for those infected or affected. That's love in action.

Christians are called to love and to care for one another: 'A new command I give you: Love one another. As I have loved you, so you must love one another. By this everyone will know that you are my disciples, if you love one another' (John 13:34–35, New International Version). Love comes straight from the heart and not from text books.

The Church has always been an advocate for education. So, she needs to be prepared to engage in qualitative research for assessment, developing a deeper sense of the worries, concerns and experiences around HIV and AIDS in the community.

The Church can also develop informal community conversations that create safe and non-threatening spaces to address stigma and discrimination, access to testing, care, comfort, treatment and the social concerns of those affected not only in relation to HIV and AIDS, but more generally by addressing ignorance, worry, blame, shame and exclusion.

Churches could start support groups for people who are infected with or directly affected by HIV and AIDS. Such a group could be regular and biblically-based, meeting where people can share their stories, pray for healing of bodies/minds, make friends and even learn new skills in a non-threatening environment.

Churches could provide appropriate training in counselling skills for interested people, so as to carry out supervised and confidential in-house counselling. Above all, the Church should encourage its members to talk freely and ask questions about HIV-AIDS, especially among young people.

Every Church should encourage members to be tested for HIV. Leaders should emphasise the importance of knowing one's HIV status and being tested at least once. At-risk groups should be encouraged to test more frequently. The Church should always remember to have a positive attitude towards HIV-positive people. Those who are HIV-negative should stay negative; while those who are HIV-positive should avoid transmitting the virus to others.

Church leaders should always lead by example. By that, I mean leaders should take the lead in having an HIV test as this will go a long way towards reducing the stigma of being tested for HIV. They should always remember that a test result should only be made public if the individual in question is comfortable about doing so.

Another thing that might be helpful is the creation of a local church health ambassadorial position. The occupant of this position should be a Christian with a passion for HIV and AIDS advocacy, and should be trained in the basics of HIV and AIDS for the purpose of bridging the gap between the church and local health services. The individual should have ready-to-give information on all aspects of HIV and AIDS and related issues. After all, it ought to be easier for church members to place confidence in the judgement of their non-judgmental brethren than in a secular social worker.

CHAPTER 8
Why the Church's Involvement is Crucial

Today, there are millions of churches of all strands and denominations; some are well established and others are not. However, members are significantly influenced by their leaders who can easily disseminate to them vital information on issues and events they care about. Cognizant of such significant influence, politicians, especially in the United States, try to rally church leaders behind their causes. American church leaders are known to have largely championed the defence of traditional marriage and the campaign against abortion, for instance. Even masterminds of pyramid schemes (also known as network or multilevel marketers) are now pushing their wide-ranging products – from weight loss pills to jewellery – through church leaders.

The fact remains that spiritual leadership is the oldest form of leadership, and continues to enjoy tremendous legitimacy and following in different societies – be they developed or developing. Church leaders are, more often than not, well respected and their opinions on various socio-economic and even political issues carry a weight of importance.

But church members live, work and play in different communities where they exert varying levels of influence. Many political, business and community leaders belong to Churches, which, in some societies, constitute part of their identity and legitimacy.

In places like Latin America and sub-Saharan Africa, Church membership is to many a matter of meaning, identity and solidarity. The same is true of many African Americans, especially since the Church played a major role in the fight against slavery and racial discrimination, hence the notion of Black Liberation Theology championed by the likes of James Cone.

So, to recap, churches are vital in HIV-AIDS advocacy. For the following reasons.
   a) Church participation/membership is, arguably, larger than that of any other movement. The Church has the power to massively mobilise people for any assignment. Its reach is huge as churches can be found in the remotest places on earth.
   b) For the most part, the Church is devoid of typical bureaucracy, thus enhancing her ability to mobilise quickly.
   c) Regardless of what some may say, the Church continues to be at the

forefront of development education and infrastructure. This is evident in the number of schools and hospitals owned and run by churches of all denominations around the world.

d) The Church has a mandate from its original founder to make disciples of all nations: 'Therefore go and make disciples of all nations, baptising them in the name of the Father and of the Son and of the Holy Spirit.' Jesus Christ Himself created the Church and gave us His authority to do good in the world. He authorised His followers to go into the world in the Great Commission. He said: 'All authority is given to Me in heaven and earth... therefore you go" (Matthew 28:19, New International Version).

What can a Christian do regarding HIV and AIDS?

- A Christian can choose to be open in talking about the disease to another Christian or a church group, or even be actively involved with community conversation initiatives.
- A Christian can explore non-threatening ways of delivering awareness messages to peer and other groups, carefully highlighting the causes and consequences of HIV and AIDS while stressing the dangers of stigma and discrimination. A Christian can wholeheartedly befriend someone who is HIV-positive and, by so doing, help reduce the impact of stigma and discrimination.

Tested prevention approach

More and more young people these days are at high risk of HIV infection than ever. Plenty of data shows that abstinence from sexual encounters before marriage, while not an easy option and tending to go against popular culture, is a proven method for prevention of HIV infection.

Another way the Church can add to the message of abstinence is to teach and promote gender equality and respect for women. Men and boys should be mentored and encouraged to respect the views and virtues of women and children, underscoring the truism that all were created equal in the image of God. Also, faithfulness to one's partner should be encouraged as it can greatly reduce unnecessary risk of sexually transmitted diseases, including HIV.

CHAPTER 9
Myths and Misconceptions about HIV and AIDS

Since the discovery of HIV, the pandemic has continued to be shrouded in many myths and misconceptions. However, scientists and researchers unravel these myths as they learn more about the disease. I have listed just a few of these myths below:

Myth No. 1: People are to blame for their HIV status.
Fact: Anyone and everyone can become HIV-positive. The virus can be contracted through various means. There is no evidence to suggest that anyone has ever purposefully become infected by the virus. Besides, being blamed can significantly lower a person's self-esteem and make it harder to gain support and to recover.

Myth No. 2: A pastor, priest or minister cannot contract HIV.
Fact: Every human being is at risk, including religious leaders.

Myth No. 3: A pastor, priest, minister who is HIV-positive is promiscuous.
Fact: That is not the case as there are other ways to become infected, e.g. transfusion by infected blood products.

Myth No. 4: A lay church member who is HIV-positive cannot be a leader in a church.
Fact: Yes, they can be leaders, and why not?

Myth No. 5: Pastors cannot perform marriages/funerals for those who are HIV-positive.
Fact: Yes, pastors can perform marriages/funerals for them.

Myth No. 6: People living with AIDS cannot get married.
Fact: Yes, they can still get married. However, they will need to learn how to manage their sexual lives so as to lead their lives to the full.

Myth No. 7: People living with AIDS cannot have healthy babies.
Fact: Yes, they can, but they will need to learn how this can happen.

Myth No. 8: People can contract HIV by being around people who are HIV-positive.
Fact: HIV is not spread through touch, sweat, tears or saliva. You cannot catch the virus by breathing the same air as someone who is HIV-positive, sharing the

same communion cup, being baptised in the same pool or baptistery, touching a toilet seat or door handle after an HIV-positive person, hugging, kissing, or shaking hands with someone who is HIV-positive.

You will also not contract the virus by cooking together or by sharing eating utensils or exercise equipment at the gym with an HIV-positive person. However, you can contract it through contact with infected blood, semen, vaginal fluid, or mother's milk.

Myth No. 9: I can contract HIV from mosquitoes.

Fact: No, studies show no evidence to support this. When insects bite, they do not inject the blood of the last person or animal they stung. Also, the virus can only live for a short time inside an insect.

Myth No. 10: Because I'm receiving treatment, I can't spread the HIV virus.

Fact: No, it is still very important to continue to practice safe sex so you don't make someone else HIV-positive.

Myth No. 11: Most people with AIDS die quickly.

Fact: Not necessarily. In fact malnutrition kills more people every year than AIDS, malaria and tuberculosis combined. One child dies every five seconds from hunger-related causes.

Myth No. 12: People who are HIV-positive have a death sentence hanging over them.

Fact: No. Antiretroviral drugs are improving and extending the lives of many people who are HIV-positive. They can live much longer, normal and productive lives.

Myth No. 13: People living with HIV/AIDS are a burden and do not contribute to the community.

Fact: No. Great numbers of important public figures, such as doctors, nurses, clergy, musicians, scientists, etc. are living with HIV/AIDS and are still contributing to the community. The flip side of that is there are also many people living with HIV/AIDS who would like to work but are not always given the opportunity.

CHAPTER 10
The Case for Condoms
(Rev Canon Dr Gideon B Byamugisha)

Two issues generally surface in Christian debates about condoms and their role in the prevention of HIV and other sexually transmitted infections, as well as the prevention of unwanted, unplanned, untimely and unsafe pregnancies. One is about efficacy and effectiveness. The other is the fear that popularising condom use for the prevention of HIV and sexually transmitted diseases (STDs) and making condoms readily accessible and affordable will encourage early sexual activity among adolescents (promiscuity) and extra–marital sex among adults (adultery), both of which are immoral in front of God and society. I will deal with each of the arguments in turn.

Efficacy and effectiveness
It is true that individual skill and compliance in condom use and disposal are required for condoms to be effective in HIV, STD and unsafe pregnancy prevention. Most times, however, critics of the role of condoms in prevention cite worse-case-scenario estimates of condom efficacy and focus on stories and studies that include persons who take on condom use incorrectly, inconsistently or after infection. Also, assertions that minimise the potential efficacy of condoms may be self–fulfilling prophecies, resulting in condoms being used with less care and consistency by those who lack the moral, spiritual and theological conviction and support to inform and sustain their use, as well as by those who do not believe them to be effective.

Contrary to what is popularly but inaccurately said about condom efficacy and effectiveness, many evidence-based studies are now available to show that correct and consistent use of condoms among the most at-risk, most vulnerable and most affected populations, families and communities could prevent nearly all of the sexually transmitted infections in persons with one sexual partner, and more than half of those among persons with multiple partners. Such a reduction could, in addition to gains from abstinence, help bring down HIV infections and transmissions in countries where millions of people are already carrying the virus but are busy marrying and remarrying each other and (*in the absence of good programs for prevention from mother-to-child transmission*) producing HIV-positive children, families and communities.

In such circumstances, church leaders, congregations and other people of faith who have a theological mandate, moral duty and ethical imperative to preserve, protect and defend life against life-threatening, life-taking and life-wasting occurrences like HIV infection should:

- teach about the advantages of condom use and the consequences of inconsistent condom use, condom misuse, condom abuse and condom non-use in the context of HIV and AIDS
- advocate for the correct and consistent use of condoms among HIV sero-positive, sero-discordant and sero-status 'blind' sexual partners
- not condone both unlawful and unsafe sex
- not 'nod' in self-justification and self-righteousness when millions of God's people who are already HIV-positive continue to infect our daughters and sons, their own wives and husbands and their own children in a manner that will wipe out the families and communities churches have always tried to protect
- ensure that love and faithfulness are not only judged and measured by not committing adultery and fornication, but also by efforts taken (or not taken) to protect one's spouse, one's children and one's community members from infection
- produce theologies and messages that reduce or eliminate the stigma attached to condom use
- help in action and advocacy to establish (a) reliable and affordable HIV testing facilities, (b) condom education and supply services for those who must use them, and (c) effective referral systems for more access to HIV treatment and prevention services.

Fear that condoms will encourage immorality

In many communities and countries, many people with HIV prevention and family planning needs are still denied access to condom education and skill development. This is usually because some leaders, communities and congregations of faith believe that such education and skill development will actually encourage people to increase their sexual activity. In fact, the reverse is true. Good quality education in sexual, reproductive and family health issues leads, among other things, to (a) lower levels of unsafe and unlawful sexual involvement, (b) fewer pregnancies that are too early, too close, too frequent, too numerous and too unsafe, and (c) lower levels of sexually transmitted infections.

Many people assert that those who promote condom use among HIV-positive, discordant and sero-status 'blind' partners are condoning sexual intercourse outside of marriage; there are two objections to this assertion, one theological and the other scientific.

Theologically, giving advice on safe sex is not the same thing as giving advice on safer sin.

My insisting that one protects oneself and others from HIV infection is a moral duty, theological imperative and ethical responsibility that does not in any way involve condoning or even approving of any personal behaviour, group activity or community practice deemed by the church, mosque or temple as 'sinful'.

On the contrary, it is an attempt to protect life, defend life and prevent sin – thou shalt not kill, rob or destroy life through unsafe sex, or indeed through any other harmful deed. Condom education and condom promotion in the context of HIV infections, transmissions, illnesses and deaths is something any Christian can be involved in with a clear conscience, as part of the work of the Church, in line with Exodus 3:7–10; Nehemiah 4:11–14; Isaiah 65:17–25; Matthew 25: 31–46; Luke 4:18–19; John 10:10 and Revelation 21:1–4. Every one of us has a moral duty to protect self and neighbour from HIV and from any other life-taking activity, unless we wish to protest to God's commandment to love others as we love ourselves by angrily shouting 'I AM NOT MY BROTHER'S OR SISTER'S KEEPER.'

In the HIV context, morality, duty, theological imperative and ethical responsibility demand that where one will abandon sexual activity before, within and outside of marriage. Also, in situations where one is either HIV-positive, sero-discordant or 'blind' about one's HIV status and/or that of one's sexual partner, condom use should be adopted correctly and consistently.

In summary:
- No one has a right to take away or reduce the quality of someone else's life, not even their own (Genesis 9:5; Deuteronomy 4:9 and Job 2:9–10).
- To refuse to give advice on safer sex – should such an opportunity present itself – might as well be regarded as 'sinful' since it is tantamount to shying away from the Church's mission to protect and preserve bodies and nourish souls.
- Condom use must never replace sexual morality and sexual morality must never disregard condom use in the context of HIV infections, transmissions, illnesses and deaths.
- We should be able to agree that premarital sex, extra-marital sex and unprotected sex among HIV-positive, discordant and sero-status 'blind' persons are all morally wrong and equally sinful if they lead to

spiritual, physical and socio-economic vulnerability.

Two moral messages on sex should be:
1. Do not engage in premarital sex, adultery and prostitution.
2. Do not put yourself and others at risk of HIV infection and transmission.

From a Christian point of view, it seems that a six-pronged HIV prevention message is necessary to save the world from moral disaster regarding the sexual transmission of HIV:
1. encouraging abstinence among both the married and unmarried in situations where the HIV sero-statuses of one or both of the sexual partners cannot be established as HIV-negative
2. encouraging mutual faithfulness among sexual partners who know each other as being HIV-negative
3. encouraging safer sex and condom use among HIV-positive, sero-discordant and sero-status 'blind' sexual partners
4. popularising systematic antiretroviral treatment as a means of reducing viral loads to undetectable levels so that one's risk of passing on the virus among the treated is significantly reduced and effectively eliminated
5. fornication, adultery and prostitution are sinful, with or without condoms
6. in sexual relations, continuing to preach against the five sexual evils – fornication/promiscuity, adultery, prostitution, defilement and rape; the AIDS epidemic requires that we do not subtract from the five, but instead preach against two additional sexual evils – murder and suicide through not abstaining and not using condoms correctly and consistently in situations where one or both of the sexual partners are HIV-positive, discordant or sero-status 'blind'.

CHAPTER 11
What would Jesus do about HIV and AIDS?

'What would Jesus do?' is a good question for every area of life. In recent times, the slogan 'what would Jesus do' (WWJD) has become a phenomenon among young people across the Christian world, especially in the USA. Young people can be seen wearing WWJD bracelets, rings, necklaces and t-shirts. The slogan is linked to Charles Sheldon, a Kansas Congregational Church minister's 1896 novel called *In His Steps*: *What would Jesus do?;* also Janie Tinklenberg, a youth leader at Calvary Reformed Church, Holland, Michigan who read the book 93 years later.

The overall emphasis of WWJD is to encourage Christians, especially the young ones, to pledge themselves earnestly and honestly for an entire year; not to do anything without first asking the question, 'What would Jesus do?'

However, there are some people who think there may be potential problems with that simple but thought-provoking question. In their view, we do not really know what Jesus would do were He to be present in person today. In as much as we cannot be emphatically sure about what Jesus would do, helpful examples abound through the records of his life in the Bible and we can glean much from those.

Since we cannot know *precisely* what Jesus would do, even in cases like HIV and AIDS, in our world today, suffice it to say that a lot of misconceptions can be avoided if we simply kept this question at the forefront of all that we say, think, and do about HIV and AIDS as a Church.

Jesus and the leper
On a trip to an African country, I came face to face with a stranded and abandoned colony of lepers and my heart bled as I saw fellow humans (children, mothers and fathers) abandoned to die just because of their physical condition in a country that prides itself on its involvement in the great move of God.

These folks were left to beg in order to survive in a land boasting of plenty. Thus, I was left to wonder about the effect of the gospel in that nation when there is such a great divide and stigmatisation in every area.

The above situation wasn't any different from the time of Christ, though the world is supposed to have moved on after 2000 years. In the Bible, we find a similar story told of Jesus and a leper; the latter went out of his way, contrary to the law of the day, to ask to be cleansed. 'A man with leprosy came to him and begged him on his knees, "If you are willing, you can make me clean." Filled with compassion, Jesus reached out his hand and touched the man. "I am willing," He said. "Be clean!" Immediately the leprosy left him and he was cured' (Mark 1:40–41).

Jesus gave the lepers and any of the social outcasts of His day Himself. He came to their homes, their parties, their weddings. He healed their children and drank with them. He touched the untouchable people. He welcomed those stigmatised by the temple leaders and welcomed them publicly.

And yes! That's what Jesus would do if he were here today, physically. I believe Jesus is expecting the Church to go the extra mile and love people living with HIV and AIDS with His love, care for them with His care. As He said in St John's gospel, 'I tell you the solemn truth, the person who believes in me will perform the miraculous deeds that I am doing, and will perform greater deeds than these, because I am going to the Father' (John 14:12, New English Translation).

The Good Samaritan

Historically, the Jews and the Samaritans were pronounced enemies. The Jews considered the Samaritans to be ceremoniously unclean, social outcasts, heretics, half-breeds and ethnic traitors, generally seen as undesirable. The phrase 'Good Samaritan' was an oxymoron as there were no 'good' Samaritans, according to the Jewish people at that time; in that context, the concept itself was as foreign to the Jews as the Samaritans were themselves. But one among them was able to look past the racial, cultural and societal stigma to the injured man who needed help, love, comfort and friendship.

This 'good' Samaritan went out of his way to give freely of his money to help a man who was not only a stranger but an enemy from a different country. In this story, Jesus encouraged his followers to emulate the Samaritan.

Often, we think of neighbours as the people who live down the street where we live but on this occasion Jesus meant it to include all mankind, regardless of their physical condition which in today's context would include HIV and AIDS. 'Love your neighbour' means loving all persons, everywhere – not just our friends, allies, countrymen and those physically perfect (Luke 10:30–34).

We are called to put our faith into practice and to truly love our neighbours, especially those less fortunate.

Jesus asked, "Which of these three do you think was a neighbour to the man who fell into the hands of robbers?" The expert in the law replied, "The one who had mercy on him." Jesus told him, "Go and do likewise" (Luke 10: 25–37).

It is important, therefore, to remember our oneness in the sight of God as members of the human family and that we are not our labels. God expects more from us, because examples of how to love one another have been set for us and it is our duty as Christians to live out that example.

These days, it is easy to talk about what Jesus would do, we wear the WWJD bracelets and necklaces but only God knows what we really want to do. We often don't want to touch, we shut the door behind those we think do not deserve the expression of the love of God; we send them away to go and find a cure first and then *maybe* they can fit into our invented mould.

Remember Jesus said, 'And the King will say, "I tell you the truth, when you did it to one of the least of these my brothers and sisters, you were doing it to me" ' (Matthew 25:40, New Living Translation, 2007).

The Church needs to stop adding to the stigma felt by those who are infected or affected by HIV and AIDS and start loving, caring and welcoming them as children of God.

That way, the process of healing will be quick and easy because He says very soon 'He [Jesus] will wipe every tear from their eyes, and there will be no more death or sorrow or crying or pain. All these things are gone forever' (Revelation 21:4, New Living Translation, 2007).

CHAPTER 12
What can the Church do?

What can the Church do? Or rather, what should the Church do? That's a crucial question every Christian needs to ask. Since the Church has such a great potential to reach people on a massive scale and the ability to influence positive behaviour within its community, it is important for her to take a full lead in the fight against HIV and AIDS, especially the issue of stigma.

According to Pastor Patricia Sawo who herself is living with the virus, 'the church has been known to do very good works when it comes to HIV and AIDS, but somehow we find out that our dealings with people living with HIV and AIDS and the continuing prevalence of HIV is alarming.

'Poverty also has a very big impact on HIV and, having grown up in poverty and yearning to come out of it and having been faced with the diseases and stigma, I come out of it as somebody who speaks the language of the church leaders.'

Christian leaders, irrespective of their HIV status (positive or negative), do need to take seriously the fight against the stigmatisation of people living with or affected by HIV and AIDS. Only then can there be true success.

Practical Suggestions
The following are six practical suggestions given by informed persons on ways in which the Church can combat the stigma:
1. Stop seeing AIDS as an 'us' and 'them' issue: AIDS is in the Church.
2. Base HIV and AIDS education on people's real experiences, not on wishful thinking.
3. Encourage theological and ethical reflection on HIV and AIDS.
4. Welcome people living with HIV and AIDS as a valuable resource.
5. Build welcoming, non-stigmatising communities.
6. Break the conspiracy of silence.

Epilogue

Like Jesus Christ, Christians all over the world have a God-given responsibility to contribute to the fight against HIV and AIDS stigma, given that they have no moral or theological justification to do otherwise, regardless of how the disease was acquired. The Church needs to acknowledge her own failure in the past and to desist from judgemental attitudes and/or unethical practices towards those who are infected or affected by HIV and AIDS.

There is also a need for the Church to recognise the fact that HIV and AIDS are like a monster and therefore cannot be tackled alone without the help of those who have continued to labour to bring the pandemic under control. The Church needs to acknowledge what she can now do to mobilise her numerous networks of resources around the world. Only then can the true meaning of God's love for the people manifest. 'For God so loved the world that He gave his one and only Son, that whoever believes in Him shall not perish but have eternal life' (John 3:16). 'The thief comes only to steal and kill and destroy; I have come that they may have life, and have it to the full' (John 10:10).

Finally, Christians must also see themselves as bearers of a message of comfort to the hurting world. The Bible says, 'How beautiful on the mountains are the feet of those who bring good news, who proclaim peace, who bring good tidings, who proclaim salvation, who say to Zion, "Your God reigns!" ' (Isaiah 52:7).

Though some people reading this publication may not be infected or affected, it is good to remember that we are all at risk, no matter what ethnicity or race; we are all at risk because we are all human.

About the Author

Since the XIV International AIDS Conference (Barcelona, 2002) the author, who served as a volunteer during the conference, has developed a passion for those infected and affected by the HIV and AIDS pandemic. He has since then determined to use his position as a minister of religion to bring the fight against HIV and AIDS stigma to the Church front.

The author continues to travel between the UK and Africa to inform and acquaint Christians with the anti-stigma message through the gospel, employing Biblical stories to illustrate his points through non-academic workshops and seminars on the subject.

The author lives in Scotland and serves as a Church of God Chaplaincy Coordinator, Coordinator for the Jubilee Social Centre, Sailors' Society Honorary Chaplain and a Member of the Christian Connection for International Health.

He has attended and participated in major conferences and workshops on the subject and is keen to see Church leaders everywhere take the matter of HIV and AIDS more seriously. He accepts invitations to speak to church groups, community groups and statutory bodies.

Author's Note

HIV and AIDS is a global situation and as such, languages used in this book may appear similar to other previous publications but it is important readers understand that as in all disciplines, there are professional languages of which ownership cannot be claimed. Where possible, I have endeavoured to give credit but this is not always possible in all cases.

Sources

Cree, V. E. - It's Good to Go for a Test (University of Edinburgh UK May 2008).

The CCIH Forum Issue # 11 October 2001.

AIDS FOR AIDS publications 2001/2002.

Global AIDS ALLIANCE publications.

Prevention of Mother-to-Child Transmission of HIV-1 The role of Nevirapine (Wordsmiths, Somerset UK 2001).

Communicating is a key factor in halting the spread of HIV/AIDS (John Hopkins University publication).

Speak out about HIV/AIDS (Mission Education Methodist Church House) England UK).

Paterson, G. - CHURCH, AIDS & STIGMA Discussion Paper 002.

Joko, L. - Reducing Stigma Anglican Church of Southern Africa HIV and AIDS Office.

Beacon of Hope Survey of TEKAN-related churches, July/August 2001, unpublished).

TEKAN, Jos, Nigeria.

Smith-Frith, Terry-Ann - http://www.yardflex.com/ archives/002980.html

http://www.who.int/mediacentre/news/notes/2007/np05/en/

Most scripture passages used are from the New International Version of the Bible unless otherwise indicated.